SPIDERS FROM SPACE

by Stan Cullimore
Illustrated by Aleksandar Sotirovski

IGNITE

00687

Titles in Ignite

Badger Publishing Limited
Oldmedow Road, Hardwick Industrial Estate,
King's Lynn PE30 4JJ
Telephone: 01438 791037

www.badgerlearning.co.uk

Spiders from Space ISBN 978 1 84926 963 6

First edition © 2012
This second edition © 2014

Text © Stan Cullimore 2012
Complete work © Badger Publishing Limited 2012

Publisher: Susan Ross
Senior Editor: Danny Pearson
Designer: Fiona Grant
Illustrator: Aleksandar Sotirovski

Contents

Vocabulary:

vanished   frowned

peered   shaken

soldier   rocket

Main characters:

Tony

Jill

a soldier

CHAPTER 1

New laptop

Tony and Jill were at school. They were sitting on a bench.

Tony had a bag with him. "Look at my new laptop," he said. "It's the best."

He put his hand into his bag and took out his new laptop.

Jill checked it out. "It looks great," she said, "but what's that?" She pointed at the side of the laptop.

There was something moving. Jill smiled. "It looks like a big spider."

Tony looked. He jumped up.
"You're right. What's it doing there?"

"It looks like it's trying to get inside your laptop," said Jill. "Why is it trying to do that?"

"I don't know, and I don't care," said Tony, dropping his bag. "I HATE spiders."

"It's not just any old spider," said Jill. "It's a dirty-great big one."

She took a closer look at it. "What do you think, Tony?"

"I just want it to go away and leave my laptop alone!" said Tony.

The spider stopped moving and suddenly vanished.

"It's OK," said Jill, "it's gone. You can relax now."

CHAPTER 2

Spider trouble

After school, Jill and Tony went to the park. Tony put his bag down.

Suddenly the spider came out of his bag.

"I thought it had gone!" groaned Tony.

The spider made a hissing noise.

"I didn't know that spiders could make noises like that," said Jill.

Tony jumped away from his bag. "Spiders can't make noises like that," he said, with fear in his eyes.

Jill picked up the bag. She had a good, long look at the spider again.

Tony gulped. "Can you just get rid of it!" he pleaded.

Jill shook her head. "I don't think it is a spider, you know."

"Then what is it?" asked Tony.

He moved back towards Jill.

"Have a look," said Jill.

She picked up the spider. She held it up for Tony to see.

The spider looked at Tony. It made the noise again. Tony screamed and jumped backwards.

"Don't be stupid," said Jill. "It's not a real spider."

"Then what is it?" frowned Tony.

"I think it's a machine," said Jill.

"Really?" asked Tony.

"Yeah," nodded Jill, "take a closer look."

Tony took a few steps towards Jill and peered at the spider. There were wires coming out of its sides.

"You're right," he said at last. "That's not a real spider at all."

CHAPTER 3

Look again

Tony took the spider from Jill. He had a look at it again. "It looks like a robot, you know. A very small robot."

"I think you're right," nodded Jill.

"I've seen things like this on the internet," said Tony. "The army use small robots like this to spy on people."

He held up the spider and shook it.

"I don't think you should shake it like that," warned Jill.

"Why not?" asked Tony.

"I don't think robots like being shaken," said Jill.

The spider robot looked at Tony. Its eyes went red. Then it opened its mouth.

Red stuff shot out of its mouth. The red stuff hit Tony in the face.

Tony screamed. "Aagh! Help! It burns!"

He dropped the spider robot. Jill got
out a tissue. She wiped the red stuff off
Tony's face.

Jill looked down at the spider robot.

She lifted up her foot. Then she
stamped her foot down hard on the
spider robot. She stamped on it again
and again.

The spider robot fell apart.

Tony looked down at the spider robot. "I'm glad you did that," he said, "but the army may not be very happy. We should take it to that army base down the road," he said. "It must come from there."

CHAPTER 4

Army base

When they got near to the army base, Tony put the bits of spider robot on the floor.

"I hope they don't mind that I stamped on it," said Jill. Tony smiled. He looked down at the spider robot.

He stopped smiling. "How is it doing that?"

"What's it doing?" asked Jill.

"Have a look," said Tony.

Jill looked. The spider robot was putting itself back together again.

A green light flashed on its head. Jill and Tony heard a crack in the air...

"What was that?" asked Tony.

"It came from the sky," said Jill, "Look!"

They both looked up.

A small rocket was falling from the sky.

It landed next to the bits of the broken spider robot.

There was another crack. The rocket opened up.

Lots more spider robots came out of the rocket. They all had green lights flashing on their heads.

"This doesn't look good," said Jill.

"Didn't I tell you that I didn't like spiders," said Tony.

"Yes you did," said Jill "and I don't like these kind, either."

The spider robots all started moving towards Jill and Tony.

Tony and Jill kicked out at the spider robots. But it was no good. There were too many of them.

"I think we should make a run for it," said Jill.

"So do I," said Tony. They turned and fled.

The spider robots chased them, but Tony and Jill had a head start.

"There's the army base!" shouted Jill.

They sprinted across the road with a huge group of spider robots hot on their heels.

As they ran, they saw a poster showing one of the spider robots. "What does it say?" shouted Jill.

"It says that if anyone finds one of these spiders, they must tell the army," explained Tony.

"That's what we're trying to do," replied Jill. "COME ON – HURRY UP!"

If you spot these...

Call the **ARMY**

Please call us on 1462 789 204

CHAPTER 5

Secret robots?

Tony and Jill ran into the army base.

They saw a man walking down the road. He was a soldier and he was carrying a big thing that looked like a gun.

Tony and Jill ran up to him.

"We have seen some of your spider robots," shouted Tony.

"How many did you see?" asked the soldier.

"Lots and lots of them," said Tony.

"They came out of a rocket that fell from the sky," said Jill.

"Where are they now?" asked the soldier.

"Right there!" cried Tony, pointing at the large group of spiders racing down the road towards them.

The soldier pulled out the big thing that looked like a gun. It was a flame-thrower. He aimed it at the spiders and fired.

Huge flames shot out of it. The spiders tried to get away from the flames, but they weren't fast enough.

With a loud hissing noise they were all destroyed.

"Don't tell any of your friends about this," said the soldier, leading Tony and Jill out of the army base.

"Why not?" asked Jill.

"Is it because they're secret robots?" asked Tony.

The soldier shook his head. "These things aren't army robots at all," he said. "They're alien spiders from space."

Facts about spiders

Spiders belong to the arachnid family. If someone is scared of spiders then it is said they suffer from arachnophobia.

The biggest spider in the world is the Giant Bird-eating spider. It has the leg span of a normal classroom ruler (30 cm).

The smallest spider is the Patu, and you can fit ten of them on the end of a pencil.

Spiders' silk is one of the strongest materials in the world. Scientists think that if they collected the same weight of spider web as a piece of steel, the spider's web would be much stronger.

There are more than 40,000 different types of spider.

Most spiders only live for a year but it has been known for some types of tarantulas to live to 25 years or longer.

Some spiders can walk on water. The Raft spider lies next to water edges with its two front feet resting on the water, feeling for vibrations. When its prey is close, it skates across the top of the water and catches its victim for food.

Nobody has discovered any spiders from space... yet!

Questions

Where was the first spider spotted?

Where did Jill and Tony go after school?

What came out of the spider's mouth?

Where did Tony and Jill run to?

Do you think there will be more spiders from space?